Walkt

This is

This i
called
the picture?

Read the title, pointing to each word in turn.

Walkthrough

This is the back cover.

This is the blurb. The blurb tells us something about the story.

Let's read it.
'What will happen to Josie's kite?'

Does the picture give you a clue?

Walkthrough

This is the title page.

Read the title, pointing at each word in turn.

What has happened to the kite in the picture?

How might the kite have got free?

What might happen in this story?

1

Walkthrough

This story is told in pictures only.

Where are Josie and her dad going? (*the park*)

What might Josie and Dad be going to do?

Summarise the page in 'storybook language'. (*One day, Josie and her dad went to the park. Josie wanted to fly her kite ...*)

2

Walkthrough

Where is Josie running with the kite? (*up the hill*)

Summarise the page in 'storybook language'.

3

Observe and Prompt

Language Comprehension

Check the children:

- can identify with the main character
- describe what is happening in both pictures
- can suggest what the characters might be saying.

Walkthrough

What is happening in the picture?

How do you know it is windy? (*scarf blowing, leaves flying around*)

Summarise the page in 'storybook language'.

4

4

Walkthrough

How do you think the kite got away?

Where might the kite be going?

What might happen next?

Summarise the page in 'storybook language'.

5

Language Comprehension

Check the children:

- notice how the story has moved on
- can describe what is happening in the pictures
- notice what is in the background on page 5
- can suggest what the characters might be saying/feeling.

Walkthrough

Tell children the girl is called Tilly.

What are the three characters trying to do?

What might they be saying?

Summarise the page in 'storybook language'.

6

Walkthrough

Tell children the boy is called Ravi.

What do you think will happen next?

Summarise the page in 'storybook language'.

7

👁 Observe and Prompt

Language Comprehension

Check the children:

- can describe what is happening in the picture
- can identify with the different characters
- can suggest what the different characters might be saying/thinking
- can suggest what might happen next – is there more than one possibility?

Walkthrough

How has the story ended?

What might Josie be saying to Ravi?

What might happen next?

Bring the story to a close using 'storybook language'.

Observe and Prompt

Language Comprehension

Check the children:

- can describe what is happening in the picture
- can suggest what Josie might be saying
- can bring the story to a close – using suitable 'storybook language'.

8